To Jack Bedford Barnard

KINGFISHER
An imprint of Larousse plc
Elsley House, 24-30 Great Titchfield Street
London W1P 7AD

First published by Kingfisher 1996
2 4 6 8 10 9 7 5 3 1

Text copyright © Tanis Jordan 1996
Illustrations copyright © Martin Jordan 1996

A CIP catalogue record for this book
is available from the British Library

ISBN: 1 85697 473 1

Designed by Caroline Johnson
Colour separations by Newsele Litho, Milan
Printed in Italy

Amazon Alphabet

Martin and Tanis Jordan

Kingfisher

Aa
is for
Agouti
eating Brazil nuts.

"A-goo-tee"

Bb

is for
Butterfly
fluttering by.

Cc _is for_ Caiman

drowsing in the sun.

"Kay-man"

Dd is for Dolphin
diving for fish.

E e _is for_ Eagle

ready to swoop.

Ff

is for

Frog

leaping from a leaf.

Gg *is for*

Giant Armadillo

snuffling for ants.

Hh
is for
Hummingbird
sipping nectar from a flower.

Ii *is for* Iguana
watchful and still.

"Ig-wah-na"

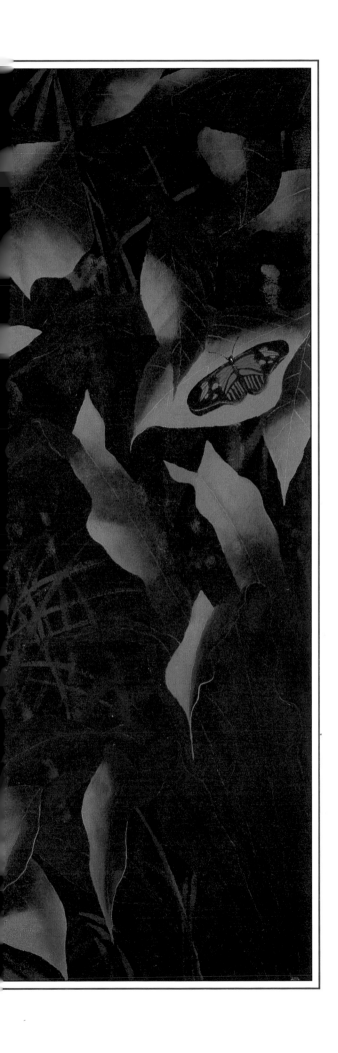

Jj

is for

Jaguar

preparing to prowl.

Kk

is for

Kinkajou

hanging by its tail.

"King-ka-*joo*"

Ll *is for* Leaf-nosed Bat

chasing a moth.

Mm *is for* Macaw

nibbling a mango.

N n *is for*

Night
Monkey

waking at dusk.

Oo
is for
Ocelot

protecting its kittens.

"Oss-e-lot"

Pp *is for* Piranha

snapping its teeth.

 "Pi-*rah*-na"

Qq *is for* Quetzal

perching to eat.

Rr

is for

Red Uakari

leaping through trees.

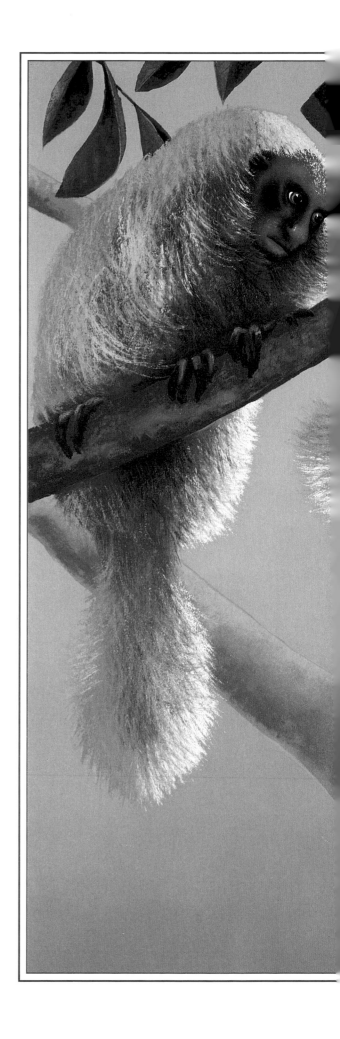

"Wack-a-ri"

Ss
is for
Sloth

grooming its coat.

Tt
is for
Toucan
with its raucous call.

Uu *is for* Umbrella Bird

with a bright red wattle.

Vv *is for* Vine Snake

on a cannonball tree.

"Peck-a-ri"

W w *is for*
White-collared Peccary
that lives in a herd.

"Peck-a-ri"

Xx _is for_ X-ray Fish

swimming past the weeds.

"*Ya* pock"

Yy *is for* *Yapok*

stalking a fish.

"*Ya* pock"

Zz is for Zorro

hidden in the trees;
the last amazing animal
in this Amazon A, B, C.

"Sor-oh'

NOTES

A

Agouti (A-*goo*-tee) *mammal*

The agouti is a rodent about the size of a rabbit. It browses on fallen fruits, nuts and seeds. Agoutis bury Brazil nuts to eat later, but often they forget where they put them and the nuts grow into Brazil nut trees. When they are in danger, agoutis scamper down into their burrows.

B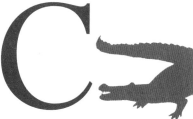

Butterfly *insect*

The Amazon has some of the biggest and most brilliant butterflies in the world. Some types fly in swarms so large they can be seen from aeroplanes. This large butterfly is called a Marpesia. The little butterfly is called an "eighty eight" because of the markings on its wings.

C

Caiman (*Kay*-man) *reptile*

Spectacled caimans are South American alligators. They grow up to 2 metres long and can live for more than fifty years. Caimans need to breathe air, so they swim with the tips of their snouts out of the water. Caimans often keep their mouths open when resting.

D

Dolphin *mammal*

River dolphins are freshwater animals; they cannot survive in the sea. Amazon river dolphins are pinker in colour than dolphins that live in the oceans. All dolphins are mammals, and have to breathe air.

E

Eagle *bird*

Harpy eagles are the biggest of all eagles. They make nests in the tops of the tallest trees and swoop down to hunt monkeys, sloths, agoutis and yapoks. They can even fly upside down beneath the crowns of the trees to pluck prey from the branches.

F

Frog *amphibian*

The latin name for this species of frog is *Hyla favosa*. It is a tree frog and has suction pads on its toes to help it grip branches and leaves. For their size, tree frogs can leap enormous distances. They feed on insects by jumping up and seizing them in the air.

G

Giant Armadillo *mammal*

Giant armadillos grow to 1.5 metres long and can weigh more than 45 kilos. They eat spiders and snakes, certain plants and insects. Using their powerful sense of smell, armadillos sniff out ant and termite nests, breaking them open with the massive claws on their front feet.

H

Hummingbird *bird*

Hummingbirds beat their wings rapidly as they hover, producing the hum that gives them their name. This frilled coquette hummingbird can also buzz like a bee. Only 6 centimetres long, it defends its territory aggressively by seeing off other hummingbirds.

I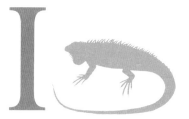

Iguana (Ig-*wah*-na) *reptile*

Green iguanas can grow up to 2 metres long. Iguanas are cold-blooded and climb to the tops of trees to warm up in the early morning sun. If in danger, an iguana will drop straight out of the tree onto the forest floor or into the river.

Jaguar *mammal*

The jaguar is the largest cat in South America with a body up to 2 metres long. It often waits for its prey on low, thick branches, dropping straight onto the back of a peccary, a deer or a tapir.

Kinkajou (King-ka-*joo*) *mammal*

The kinkajou which is related to the raccoon spends all its time in the trees. Though it uses its strong, long tail to grip, it does not leap from branch to branch. Instead, it curls its tail around branches and hangs down, leaving its hands free to reach fruits or break open bees' nests for honey.

Leaf-nosed Bat *mammal*

This leaf-nosed bat feeds on moths and other insects which it catches in flight. No one knows exactly how many species of leaf-nosed bat live in the Amazon. Some species eat frogs, birds, and lizards. Others prefer nectar from flowers.

Macaw *bird*

Hyacinth macaws eat fruit, seeds, nuts and leaves. One metre long from head to tip of tail feather, they are the largest flying parrots in the world. Macaws use their strong beaks to break open Brazil nut pods to get at the nuts inside. They nest in holes in trees.

Night Monkey *mammal*

Night monkeys are the only monkeys in the Amazon that are out and about at night. They come out from their tree holes at a precise time – fifteen minutes after the sun has set – to search for fruit and to catch flying insects to eat.

Ocelot (*Oss*-e-lot) *mammal*

The ocelot is a small cat, 1 metre long. Ocelots have between two and four kittens and they usually stay with their mothers until she has taught them to hunt for themselves. Ocelots have exceptional eyesight, excellent hearing and sensitive whiskers which they use when stalking prey.

Piranha (Pi-*rah*-na) *fish*

The red-bellied piranha is one of nearly twenty species of piranha that live in Amazon rivers. Piranhas have sharp triangular teeth and jaws powerful enough to bite through steel wire. They hunt in shoals of ten to one hundred.

Quetzal (*Ket*-sal) *bird*

The Amazonian Pavonine quetzal seen here has a shorter tail than some other species of quetzal. It lives in dense parts of the Amazon forest and feeds on insects and small fruits such as wild avocados.

Red Uakari (*Wack*-a-ri) *mammal*

The red uakari, sometimes known as the bald uakari, does not have a long tail to hold on to the branches but it is very agile, leaping from tree to tree in search of fruit, leaves, buds and seeds to eat. In the wild it has a bright red face colour but if it is kept in captivity, the red colour fades.

Sloth *mammal*

The three-toed sloth feeds mainly on cecropia leaves, its favourite food. Some sloths may stay in the same tree for years, sleeping up to eighteen hours a day. Sloths move so slowly that a plant called algae grows in the grooves of their hair and camouflages them among the leaves.

Toucan *bird*

The keel-billed toucan's call is a harsh, rasping sound. Its massive bill is sharp and strong but surprisingly light. Toucans roost in holes in trees, tucking their bills under their wings when they sleep. They like to feed on fruit and berries.

Umbrella Bird *bird*

Umbrella birds have glossy feathered crests on their heads. The male has a large red air sac called a wattle hanging from his throat with a single feather on its tip. The female has a small but not so splendid wattle. The male inflates his wattle to make a booming, hooting call.

Vine Snake *reptile*

When vine snakes hang motionless in the trees, they look like jungle lianas or vines. Unlike most snakes which glide smoothly, vine snakes move jerkily like falling vegetation. Vine snakes are slender and grow up to 1.25 metres long. They are venomous and mostly eat lizards.

White-collared Peccary (*Peck-a-ri*) *mammal*

White-collared peccaries live in herds of up to fifty, travelling through the forest foraging in the leaf litter for plants and roots. They have sharp tusks and defend themselves against enemies. One adult male calls the herd together with a sound like a cough.

X-ray Fish *fish*

X-ray fish are daring when in big shoals but in small groups they are shy and like to stay in shady places or among water plants. They are almost transparent. X-ray fish can grow up to 5 centimetres long.

Yapok (*Ya-pock*) *mammal*

Yapoks are water opossums and live along the riverbank. They have webbed feet and sensitive whiskers which they use to detect movements in the water. Female yapoks carry their young in pouches on their fronts. Even when they dive deep in the river the young stay safe.

Zorro (*Sor-oh*) *mammal*

Little is known about this animal. Zorro is the Spanish word for fox but the zorro is one of the largest of the South American wild dogs. A rare, mysterious animal, it reminds us that much still remains to be discovered about the wildlife of the Amazon.